Perseverance

Disney · PIXAR
FINDING NEMO

Adapted by Lisa Harkrader
Illustrated by the Disney Storybook Artists

Published by Louis Weber, C.E.O.
Publications International, Ltd.
7373 North Cicero Avenue, Lincolnwood, Illinois 60712

Ground Floor, 59 Gloucester Place, London W1U 8JJ
Customer Service: 1-800-595-8484 or customer_service@pilbooks.com

www.pilbooks.com

p i kids is a registered trademark of Publications International, Ltd.

ISBN-13: 978-1-4127-6238-0
ISBN-10: 1-4127-6238-3

Nemo was a clownfish. He couldn't wait to start his first day of school.

"Wake up, Dad!" he cried.

But his father, Marlin, worried about him. One of Nemo's fins was smaller than the other.

"Are you sure you want to go to school?" said Marlin.

"Yes!" Nemo wasn't going to let a small fin stop him.

Marlin took Nemo to school but stayed close by to watch.

On a field trip, Nemo's new school friends wandered away from their teacher. Nemo followed. They found a boat, and his friends dared Nemo to touch it.

Nemo paddled to the boat and swam straight into a diver! The diver caught Nemo in his net and swam back to the boat.

"Dad!" cried Nemo. "Help me!"

"I'm coming!" called Marlin.

But the boat carried Nemo away before Marlin could save him.

Marlin swam and swam. But he couldn't catch the boat. No matter how discouraged he was, Marlin wasn't about to give up. He darted toward a school of fish.

"Help me," he said looking out deep into the great big ocean. "I have to find my son."

The only fish who would listen was a blue tang named Dory. Dory didn't remember things very well, but that didn't stop her wanting to help. Together, Marlin and Dory swam off to find Nemo.

The diver who caught Nemo was a
dentist. He put Nemo in his fish
tank. Nemo met the other fish,
and a pelican named Nigel.

The dentist planned to give Nemo to his niece Darla. "Darla!" exclaimed the other fish. "She's horrible! You better get out of here fast! We'll need a plan."

The other fish knew that when the dentist cleaned the tank, he took the fish out. Once Nemo was out, he could escape to the ocean. They clogged the tank's cleaning filter and waited for the tank to get dirty.

But the dentist didn't take the fish out. Instead, he installed a new filter. Within minutes, the filter turned the tank sparkling clean.

But Nemo didn't give up!

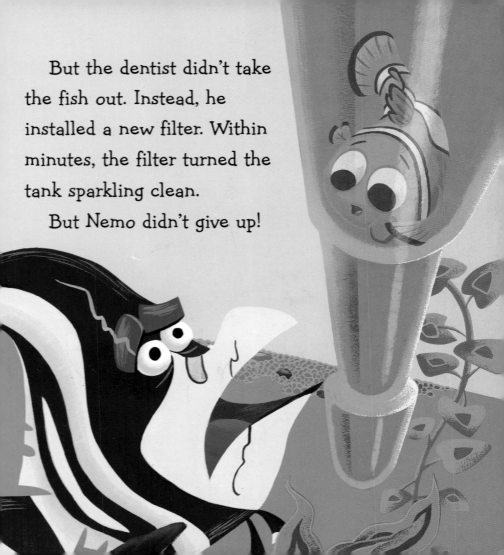

Meanwhile, Marlin and Dory had found the dentist's diving mask. On the mask was the dentist's address in Sydney, Australia: "P. Sherman, 42 Wallaby Way, Sydney." Marlin and Dory knew they had to go to Sydney to find Nemo. They braved sharks, a menacing anglerfish, stinging jellyfish, ocean currents, and the dark depths of the sea to reach Sydney. When Marlin became discouraged, Dory said, "Just keep swimming, swimming, swimming." And that's just what they did!

When horrible Darla arrived at the dentist's office, Nemo pretended to be dead. The dentist flushed Nemo down the drain.

"Don't worry," said Gill. "All drains lead to the ocean."

Nemo swam through pipes till he reached the harbor, where he found Marlin and Dory.

"Dad!" cried Nemo.

"Nemo!" cried Marlin.
Marlin had found Nemo, and Nemo had found his dad, all because they didn't give up!

Perseverance

Perseverance means never giving up!

Marlin was very scared and worried at times, but he wouldn't stop looking for Nemo — not for all the fish in the sea! And no matter how hard it was to escape the tank, Nemo wouldn't give up until he was with his father again.

When something is important to you, you need perseverance to keep swimming, swimming, swimming until you achieve your goal.